Y0-BDE-734

Good grief, more PEANUTS!®

Books by Charles M. Schulz

Peanuts
More Peanuts
Good Grief, More Peanuts!
Good Ol' Charlie Brown
Snoopy
You're Out of Your Mind, Charlie Brown!
But We Love You, Charlie Brown
Peanuts Revisted
Go Fly a Kite, Charlie Brown
Peanuts Every Sunday
It's a Dog's Life, Charlie Brown
You Can't Win, Charlie Brown
Snoopy, Come Home
You Can Do It, Charlie Brown
We're Right Behind You, Charlie Brown
As You Like It, Charlie Brown
Sunday's Fun Day, Charlie Brown
You Need Help, Charlie Brown
Snoopy and the Red Baron
The Unsinkable Charlie Brown
You'll Flip, Charlie Brown
You're Something Else, Charlie Brown
Peanuts Treasury
You're You, Charlie Brown
You've Had It, Charlie Brown
Snoopy and His Sopwith Camel
A Boy Named Charlie Brown
You're Out of Sight, Charlie Brown
Peanuts Classics
You've Come a Long Way, Charlie Brown
Snoopy and "It Was a Dark and Stormy Night"
"Ha Ha, Herman," Charlie Brown
The "Snoopy, Come Home" Movie Book
Snoopy's Grand Slam
Thompson Is in Trouble, Charlie Brown
You're the Guest of Honor, Charlie Brown

Weekly Reader Books presents

Good grief, more PEANUTS!®

By CHARLES M. SCHULZ

HOLT, RINEHART AND WINSTON

NEW YORK · CHICAGO · SAN FRANCISCO

In Canada, Holt, Rinehart and Winston of Canada, Limited

Library of Congress Catalog Card Number: 56-11637

ISBN: 0-03-029920-9
Printed in the United States of America

This book is a presentation of
Weekly Reader Books.
Weekly Reader Books offers
book clubs for children from
preschool to young adulthood.

For further information write to:
Weekly Reader Books
1250 Fairwood Ave.
Columbus, Ohio 43216

CHARLIE BROWN

VIOLET

SNOOPY

PATTY

SHERMY

LUCY

SCHROEDER

BEETHOVEN

'PIG-PEN'

LINUS

KRINKLE

!
SCHULZ

KNOCK KNOCK..
WHO'S THERE?

FUZZ!

HUH?

FUZZ! THERE'S A PIECE OF FUZZ ON THE SIDEWALK!

OH, GOOD GRIEF..
I'M SCARED OF FUZZ! BRUSH IT AWAY, CHARLIE BROWN! BRUSH IT AWAY!

THAT'S THE SILLIEST THING I'VE EVER HEARD! FUZZ!!! GOOD GRIEF!
BRUSH IT AWAY! BRUSH IT AWAY!!

AAK!!
IT MOVED

IT'S A BUG! IT'S A BUG!
IT'S A PIECE OF FUZZ!

LET'S GO BACK THE WAY WE CAME..
WE CAN WALK CLEAR AROUND THE BLOCK SOMEDAY WHEN WE'RE OLDER
FUZZ! BRRR.
SCHULZ

!

SCHULZ
?

I'M DISCOURAGED TODAY, AND WHEN I GET DISCOURAGED, A COMIC MAGAZINE IS THE ONLY THING THAT WILL REVIVE ME

For the Kiddies
WHAT A BEAUTIFUL GORY LAYOUT!

For the Kiddies
THIS DRUGGIST IS AWFULLY FUSSY...HE WON'T LET YOU LOOK AT THE COMIC MAGAZINES UNLESS YOU BUY ONE...
TERROR COMICS
GEE, THE COVER CAME OFF THIS ONE...I HARDLY JERKED IT!

For the Kiddies
THOSE ON THE TOP ROW LOOK PRETTY GOOD...

WHOOPS!

HE SHOULD SELL THESE FOR HALF PRICE...WHO WANTS A MAGAZINE AFTER IT'S BEEN LAYING AROUND ON THE FLOOR?

I GUESS I'LL TAKE THIS ONE...

BOY, DID HE EVER GLARE AT ME! HE PROBABLY ISN'T FEELING WELL...
SCHULZ

OH, YOU'RE A BEAUTIFUL BALLOON!

AND YOU'RE ALL MINE.. MINE... MINE....

WHOOPS!

HEY! COME BACK HERE!

COME BACK HERE!

OH, PLEASE COME BACK, BALLOON! PLEASE!

YOU DIRTY OL' BALLOON! COME BACK HERE!!

OH, PLEASE COME BACK... PLEASE.....

YOU DIRTY BALLOON! YOU BETTER COME BACK HERE!!

OH, PLEASE! PLEASE! I'LL DO ANYTHING IF YOU'LL JUST COME BACK

OH, YOU DIRTY BALLOON! IF YOU DON'T COME BACK, I'LL..

OH, PLEASE, BALLOON! OH, PLEASE! OH,..

OH, RATS!

ONE, TWO, THREE, FOUR, FIVE...

SIXTEEN, SEVENTEEN, EIGHTEEN...

NINETY-ONE
NINETY-TWO

NINETY-THREE
NINETY-FOUR

PUFF PUFF

PUFF PUFF

PANT PANT

CHOMP! CHOMP!

Allegro
ff
Ped
SCHULZ

LET'S WALK UP TO THE DIME-STORE, LUCY, AND LOOK AT ALL THE TOYS

I THINK IT'S A LOT OF FUN EVEN IF YOU CAN'T BUY ANYTHING

LOOK HERE, LUCY... LOOK AT ALL THE LITTLE DOLLS!
?
!
10¢
15¢

ALL I CAN SEE IS THE FRONT OF THE COUNTER..
AND LOOK OVER HERE... LOOK AT THE TINY DISHES!

I MUST SAY THEY'RE PUTTING GOOD WOOD INTO 'EM THESE DAYS...
GEE...AN' LOOK OVER HERE..

NICE AND SMOOTH, TOO... GOOD JOB OF SANDING
LOOK AT ALL THE PAPER DOLLS...AND LOOK AT THOSE TOY BOATS...

I SEE THEY USED SCREWS INSTEAD OF NAILS...THAT'S A GOOD IDEA...
HERE'RE SOME TINY AIRPLANES, AND THERE'S A TINY FIRE ENGINE!

WE'LL HAVE TO DO THAT AGAIN SOME DAY, HUH, LUCY?
SURE...CALL FOR ME AGAIN IN ABOUT FOUR YEARS!
SCHULZ

?

GROWF!

ARF ARF

ARF!
ARF!
ARF!
ARF!

WHAM!

SCHULZ

POOR OL' 'PIG-PEN'... I'LL BET HE COULD RAISE A CLOUD OF DUST RUNNING ON A SIDEWALK!

HERE, CHARLIE BROWN... I'VE GOT A PIECE OF CANDY FOR YOU..

GEE... I CAN'T GET IT OUT OF MY POCKET.. IT'S STUCK...

THERE!
OH, GOOD GRIEF!

I'LL BRUSH THE LINT OFF FOR YOU,.. AND SCRAPE THIS OLD GUM OFF THE BEST I CAN...
I FEEL SICK

WELL, WHY DON'T YOU EAT IT?
I WILL, 'PIG-PEN', I WILL... I JUST... I.. I..

WHOOPS! I DROPPED IT!
!
GULP!
ZOOM

PSST... SNOOPY, OL' PAL... YOU'D BETTER COME HOME WITH ME, AND HAVE A DRINK OF WATER..
?
SCHULZ

O.K., THAT'S ENOUGH..TURN THE WATER OFF...

IT'S OUR DUTY TO REVIVE FULLY THE LOST ART OF MUD-PIE BAKING

SLOSH THE MUD AROUND REAL GOOD!

NOW, MIX IT UP! STIR IT AROUND! STIR IT AROUND!
I'M STILL SLOSHING!

BOY, LOOK AT THAT TEXTURE!
ISN'T IT WONDERFUL?!

WE'RE THE BEST MUD PIE BAKERS IN THIS WHOLE COUNTRY!
?

WOW! ARE YOU GIRLS EVER A MESS! WAIT UNTIL YOUR MOTHERS SEE YOU!!

WHY? WHAT'S WRONG? WE'VE GOT OUR APRONS ON!
SCHULZ

JANUARY, FEBRUARY, MARCH...

ONE TWO, THREE, FOUR, FIVE!

GOOD GRIEF! SPRING BEGAN FIVE DAYS AGO!

I GOTTA CALL SCHROEDER...I'LL BET HE DOESN'T EVEN KNOW IT...

WADDYA MEAN, Y'DON'T CARE WHAT THE CALENDAR SAYS?!

BY GOLLY, I SURE CARE WHAT THE CALENDAR SAYS!

C'MON! LET'S PLAY BALL!!
SCHULZ

HEY, LOOKIT! LOOK AT ALL THE RECORDS IN THIS BOX!
THEY MUST BELONG TO MY MOTHER AND DAD...

I DIDN'T THINK THEY EVEN HAD PHONOGRAPHS IN THOSE DAYS...

SOME OF THESE OLD RECORDS ARE REALLY FUNNY!

HERE'S ONE CALLED, "OLD ROCKIN' CHAIR'S GOT ME"
PUT IT ON...LET'S LISTEN TO IT

SAY, THAT'S A PRETTY GOOD SONG...

THERE'S ONLY ONE THING I DON'T UNDERSTAND...

WHAT IN THE WORLD IS A "ROCKING CHAIR"?
SCHULZ

WE'VE GOT TO HAVE A RIGHT FIELDER, DON'T WE? GO AHEAD.. ASK HER!
I THINK I'D ALMOST RATHER FORFEIT THE GAME!

NO GOOD CAN POSSIBLY COME OF THIS...

LUCY, HOW WOULD YOU LIKE TO BE A SUBSTITUTE?

I DON'T THINK I WOULD... I'VE ALWAYS WANTED TO BE A NURSE

THAT'S NOT WHAT I MEAN...WE'RE SHORT ONE PLAYER...WE NEED YOU FOR RIGHT FIELD
OH..

THE SUN IS PRETTY BRIGHT OUT THERE SO YOU'D BETTER WEAR THESE DARK GLASSES

EVEN THOUGH I DON'T KNOW WHAT'S GOING ON, I FEEL REAL PROFESSIONAL

THESE GLASSES WOULD BE PERFECT IF AN ECLIPSE CAME ALONG..

I'VE NEVER REALLY SEEN AN ECLIPSE..

THERE JUST MIGHT BE ONE ALL READY TO COME ALONG

BONK!

HEY, CHARLIE BROWN!

HERE...TAKE YOUR OL' DARK GLASSES... I THINK THEY'RE BAD FOR MY EYES..

THEY GIVE ME A HEADACHE!
SCHULZ

ALL RIGHT, WHO'S GOT MY BALLOON !?!

JUST WAIT UNTIL I CATCH THE PERSON WHO TOOK THAT BALLOON...BOY-O-BOY!!

SSSSSSS

LINUS, DID YOU SEE WHO TOOK MY BALLOON?!
MMBG

WELL YOU'RE JUST LUCKY YOU DIDN'T HAVE ANYTHING TO DO WITH IT...

WHEW!
SCHULZ

Pat
Pat
Pat

AH! THE FIRST SNOWBALL OF THE YEAR!

I LIKE TO BEGIN EACH WINTER BY HITTING CHARLIE BROWN RIGHT ON THE HEAD!

I CAN'T DO IT... I CAN'T DO IT...

IT'S NO USE...I JUST CAN'T DO IT...OH, BOO, HOO, HOO...HE'S SO INNOCENT...I JUST CAN'T DO IT..
?
SOB SOB SOB

I WAS GOING TO HIT YOU WITH THIS SNOWBALL, CHARLIE BROWN, BUT I'M TOO SOFT-HEARTED...
WELL, I'M GLAD YOU CHANGED YOUR MIND, LUCY...YOU'RE A GOOD GIRL..

WHAT AM I DOING? I'VE GOT TO GET HOLD OF MYSELF!

POW!

OH, IT'S GOING TO BE A GREAT WINTER!
SCHULZ

MERRY "day after Christmas"! MAY I COME IN?

YOU'LL NEVER BELIEVE THIS, I KNOW, BUT I WAS HOPING YOU'D COME OVER..

I WANT YOU TO SEE ALL THE NICE CHRISTMAS PRESENTS I GOT, CHARLIE BROWN..

LOOK! A NEW TOY PIANO!

BLACK KEYS STILL JUST PAINTED ON, I SEE...

A NEW STATUE OF BEETHOVEN..
VERY SCOWLLY..

A NEW BEETHOVEN SWEAT SHIRT...

A BEETHOVEN BALL-POINT PEN...

A TWELVE-VOLUME BIOGRAPHY OF BEETHOVEN IN COMIC-BOOK FORM...

AND A YEAR'S SUPPLY OF BEETHOVEN BUBBLE GUM!

OH, YES ... I ALMOST FORGOT... I ALSO GOT AN ELECTRIC TRAIN..

NOW, WHAT IN THE WORLD AM I GOING TO DO WITH AN ELECTRIC TRAIN?!
SCHULZ

OH, GOOD GRIEF!

WILL YOU READ ME A STORY, CHARLIE BROWN?
I'M TRAPPED... THERE'S NO USE KIDDING MYSELF... I'M TRAPPED...

WON'T YOU **PLEASE** READ ME A STORY, CHARLIE BROWN?

OH, ALL RIGHT... I - SUPPOSE WE MIGHT AS WELL GET IT OVER..

LET'S SEE WHAT THEY'VE GOT HERE...

Once upon a time they lived happily ever after. The End.

?

STORIES

HEY...
STORIES

WHAT'S ON THE REST OF THESE PAGES.... **ADVERTISING**?
SCHULZ

AS LONG AS I'M AT THIS END OF THE BLOCK, I REALLY OUGHT TO STOP IN AND SEE LINUS AND LUCY..

I HAVEN'T SEEN LINUS FOR QUITE A WHILE...

HOW'S YOUR BABY BROTHER, LUCY ?

I DON'T THINK HE'S VERY WELL... I'M WORRIED ABOUT HIM...

WHY ? HE LOOKS FINE TO ME... IN FACT, HE LOOKS VERY HAPPY

NO, I DON'T THINK SO...WATCH..

HEY, LINUS!

SEE? HE'S AWFULLY NERVOUS!
SCHULZ

THAT'S WHAT I THINK OF YOUR BOX OF COOKIES!
COOKIES

THAT'S WHAT I THINK OF YOUR OL' PIANO!
?

THAT'S WHAT I THINK OF YOUR OL' STAMP COLLECTION!

AND THAT'S WHAT I THINK OF YOUR OL' PICTURE PUZZLE!

AND THAT'S WHAT I THINK OF YOUR STUPID OL' MARBLES!

AND THAT'S WHAT I THINK OF YOUR SILLY OL' COLOR CRAYONS!

SCHULZ
I'M FRUSTRATED AND INHIBITED, AND NOBODY UNDERSTANDS ME..

IT SAYS HERE THAT IF A DOG'S NOSE IS WARM, HE PROBABLY ISN'T FEELING WELL..

VERY INTERESTING...

I WONDER IF SNOOPY'S NOSE IS WARM OR COLD?
WHY DON'T YOU FIND OUT?
?

YOU MEAN TOUCH HIS NOSE?! OH, NO...I COULDN'T DO THAT...OH, NO....I'D BE SCARED...

YOU MEAN WALK RIGHT OVER, AND TOUCH IT, DON'T YOU? OH, NO....I DON'T THINK I COULD EVER.. I'LL DO IT!

NICE DOGGIE...NICE DOGGIE...EASY...EASY NOW.. NICE DOGGIE...EASY..EASY.. EASY..EASY..EASY..
?

AH-CHOO!

HE EXPLODED!
SCHULZ

LUCK!

DUMB LUCK!!
PLUNK!

LUCK!
CLINK!

PLAIN LUCK! JUST PLAIN, DOWNRIGHT, OL' FOOL LUCK!
CLUNK!

LUCK, LUCK, LUCK!
PLINK!

WELL, THAT ENDS THE GAME, CHARLIE BROWN...UNLESS YOU'VE GOT SOME MORE MARBLES...
YOU KNOW I HAVEN'T!

YOU JUST CAN'T BEAT FOOL LUCK!
♪

LUCK! LUCK LUCK! LUCK!

BOY, CAN THAT GIRL EVER PLAY MARBLES!
SCHULZ

I DREAD COMING TO THE CORNER...I KNOW JUST WHAT'S GOING TO HAPPEN..

THE LIFE YOU SAVE MAY BE A FUSSBUDGET..

LET ME HAVE YOUR HAND, LUCY, AS WE CROSS THE STREET..

OH, NO YOU DON'T!

I KNOW YOUR KIND, CHARLIE BROWN! YOU JUST WANT TO HOLD HANDS!
OH, GOOD GRIEF! HERE WE GO AGAIN!

YOU'RE THE MOST AGGRAVATING PERSON IN THE WORLD!!

I DON'T CARE!! I'M NOT GOING TO HOLD HANDS WITH ANY BOY!

ALL RIGHT, GET RUN OVER BY A CAR THEN! CROSS THE STREET BY YOURSELF!!

WAIT A MINUTE, CHARLIE BROWN...
NOW, WHAT?

I'VE GOT AN IDEA...

SCHULZ

?

I DON'T GET IT..
?

?
?

WHY DOES LINUS SIT AROUND ALL DAY HOLDING THAT BLANKET?

IT GIVES HIM SECURITY AND HAPPINESS... DIDN'T YOU HAVE A BLANKET WHEN YOU WERE LITTLE, CHARLIE BROWN?

HERE...FEEL HOW SOFT IT IS...IT'S CALLED 'OUTING' FLANNEL..
OUTING FLANNEL?!

YOU MEAN IF I HOLD THIS NEXT TO MY CHEEK ALL DAY, I'LL BE HAPPY?
INSANELY HAPPY!!!

THAT'S THE MOST STUPID THING I'VE EVER HEARD!
!

STILL...I COULD USE A LITTLE SECURITY...

ONE YARD OF 'OUTING' FLANNEL.. AND DON'T LAUGH!!
DRY GOODS
SCHULZ

WHEW

NERVOUS ENERGY..
CHARLES M. SCHULZ

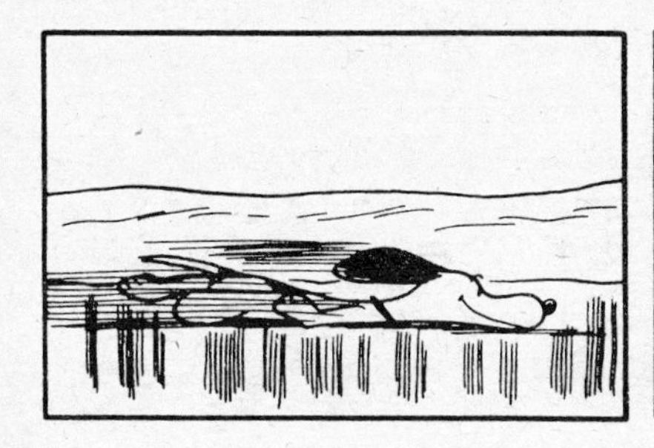

?

!

THAT'S THE WAY IT GOES...
SCHULZ

WELL, I'M UP HERE!

I'VE NEVER TRIED THIS BEFORE, YOU KNOW...

WHAT DO I DO NOW, CHARLIE BROWN?

JUST GIVE YOURSELF A LITTLE SHOVE...
THAT'S THE WAY!

DOWN YOU GO!
FASTER! FASTER!

FASTER! FASTER, LUCY! FASTER!

I DON'T THINK I'M MOVING...

SCHULZ
SOME PEOPLE JUST AREN'T ATHLETIC!
I DON'T THINK I'M MOVING AT ALL...

FACTS ARE FACTS!
PHOOEY!

WHAT DO YOU MEAN, 'PHOOEY'?
JUST WHAT I SAID ...'PHOOEY'

YOU DON'T KNOW WHAT YOU'RE TALKING ABOUT, LUCY!

IS THAT SO?!
YES, THAT'S SO!

HERE COMES CHARLIE BROWN... LET'S SEE WHAT **HE** THINKS..
WHO CARES WHAT **HE** THINKS?!

CHARLIE BROWN, WE WANT YOUR OPINION ON SOMETHING...

IS THERE A SANTA CLAUS OR **ISN'T** THERE A SANTA CLAUS?

I REFUSE TO GET INVOLVED IN A THEOLOGICAL DISCUSSION!
SCHULZ

IT'S GONE!

OF ALL THE NERVE!

LUCY'S TAKEN MY BASEBALL GLOVE AGAIN!

JUST BECAUSE I LEAVE IT ON THE FRONT SIDEWALK EVERY NIGHT, SHE THINKS IT'S PUBLIC PROPERTY!

I'M GOING TO SETTLE THIS ONCE AND FOR ALL...

HEY, YOU!!
THUMP!

?
!
KLOP!

PLUNK!

CLUMP!

OH, DO YOU WANT YOUR GLOVE BACK, CHARLIE BROWN?
NO, YOU MIGHT AS WELL KEEP IT, LUCY.... I'LL PROBABLY NEVER HAVE ANY USE FOR IT AGAIN!
SCHULZ

FROM TWENTY-TWO TO TWENTY-THREE TO TWENTY-FOUR TO TWENTY-FIVE TO TWENTY-SIX TO TWENTY-SEVEN...
?

SEE, LUCY? YOU JUST FOLLOW THE NUMBERS AROUND, AND CONNECT ALL THE DOTS...
AND THERE'S A PICTURE OF A KITTY! WELL, I'LL BE!

I NEVER KNEW THAT JUST CONNECTING DOTS COULD BE SO MUCH FUN..

I DON'T KNOW MUCH ABOUT NUMBERS, BUT I'M **SURE** I CAN CONNECT DOTS!

TUM DE TUM TE DA TE DUM

!

SCHULZ

WELL, THANKS TO THAT LAST STUPID PLAY YOU MADE, I WIN AGAIN!
RATS!

I CAN'T STAND IT...

THAT MAKES SEVEN THOUSAND GAMES IN A ROW, CHARLIE BROWN..

SEVEN THOUSAND?

I CAN'T STAND IT!!!

I'M GOING CRAZY! WHY CAN'T I WIN JUST ONE GAME?

I'M JUST NO GOOD! THAT'S IT! I'M NO GOOD! I'M NO GOOD!

I CAN'T PLAY CHECKERS, I CAN'T PLAY BASEBALL, I CAN'T PLAY FOOTBALL, I CAN'T DO ANYTHING!
THUMP! THUMP!

AND I CAN'T STAND IT!

WHY CAN'T I WIN JUST ONCE?! JUST ONCE?

WELL, ARE YOU BACK TO NORMAL?

YES, I GUESS SO... GO AHEAD..START ANOTHER GAME..
SCHULZ

Hey!

GIMME THOSE TOYS!!!

EVERYTHING'S MINE! MINE! MINE! MINE!
SIGH

HERE...I GUESS YOU CAN HAVE THIS RUBBER BAND... HAVE FUN WITH THAT..

WHAT'S GOING ON HERE?!

GIMME THAT!

I DIDN'T MEAN FOR YOU TO HAVE THAT MUCH FUN!
SCHULZ

ALL OF US GOT NICE THINGS FOR CHRISTMAS EXCEPT HIM..

IT DOESN'T MATTER IF HE'S ONLY A DOG...HE'S OUR FRIEND..

SO YOU SEE, I THOUGHT I'D BETTER TAKE UP A COLLECTION TO GET SNOOPY A LITTLE CHRISTMAS PRESENT..

WHY, HOW NICE!
YES! HOW THOUGHTFUL OF YOU, CHARLIE BROWN!

I'LL BE GLAD TO DONATE A NICKEL...
I WILL, TOO... HERE....

IT'S SO GOOD OF YOU TO BE GOING TO ALL THIS TROUBLE...
YES, AND TO BE TAKING UP YOUR OWN VALUABLE TIME
ALL I HAVE TO DO NOW IS FIND A STORE THAT'S OPEN..

GEE...THOSE GIRLS SURE SAID SOME NICE THINGS...THEY ALWAYS USED TO MAKE ME FEEL SO INFERIOR.. I GUESS THEY DON'T THINK I'M SO BAD AFTER ALL...

BOY, WHAT A DOPE THAT CHARLIE BROWN IS!
YOU CAN SAY THAT AGAIN!
SCHULZ

ARE YOU SURE, CHARLIE BROWN? ARE YOU ABSOLUTELY SURE? ARE YOU?

SIGH

LUCY, WHY DO YOU ASK ME THINGS IF YOU DON'T EVER BELIEVE ME?

OH, I BELIEVE YOU, CHARLIE BROWN..I BELIEVE EVERYTHING YOU TELL ME...

YOU DO NOT!
SURE, I DO... TELL ME SOMETHING, AND WATCH ME BELIEVE YOU..

OH, GOOD GRIEF... DON'T BE SO STUPID!
COME ON...TELL ME SOMETHING...WATCH ME BELIEVE YOU..TELL ME ANYTHING...

THE WORLD IS MADE OF SNOW
I BELIEVE YOU!

THE WORLD IS MADE OF SNOW!!

HEY, VIOLET, CHARLIE BROWN JUST TOLD ME THAT THE WORLD IS MADE OF SNOW..
CHARLIE BROWN IS OUT OF HIS MIND!
!

YOU'RE OUT OF YOUR MIND, CHARLIE BROWN!

YOU WANT ME TO 'BREAK'?
SURE, GO AHEAD.. LADIES FIRST..
WHERE'S THE CHALK?

WHAT HAPPENS IF I CLEAR THE TABLE?
THEN YOU WIN, OF COURSE..
'CLEAR THE TABLE'.. WHAT A LAUGH!

?!
!

WHAM!!

I CLEARED THE TABLE! I CLEARED THE TABLE! I WON!! I WON!

GOOD GRIEF! WHAT HAPPENED?
I THINK SHE CLEARED THE TABLE...

SCHULZ
DON'T GET TOO UPSET, CHARLIE BROWN...MAYBE NEXT WINTER YOU CAN USE IT FOR A SLED!

BAM!
BAM!

CHARGE!

KAWAM
KAWAM
ZAP!

POW!
KAZAAP!!
ZAAP!
?

WUMP!
POW! POW!
BAM! BAM! BAM!
KAWOOM!!
KAZAAP!

LUCY, CAN'T YOU AND YOUR FRIENDS PLAY A LITTLE MORE QUIETLY?
ALL RIGHT, MOTHER...

RATTLE
RATTLE

DIDN'T YOU HEAR MOTHER?!
STOP THAT AWFUL NOISE!!
SCHULZ

C'MON, SNOOPY..
C'MON, BOY..

NICE DOGGIE...
NICE SNOOPY..

?

TRY IT.... IT'S
AMAZING..

!
I FEEL KIND
OF SILLY..

?
SHHH...

YOU'RE RIGHT, LUCY...UH, HUH..

I CAN HEAR THE
OCEAN ROAR!
Oh, good
grief!!
SCHULZ

NINE HUNDRED AN' ONE..NINE HUNDRED AN' TWO...

GEE, I THOUGHT YOU'D HAVE GIVEN UP BY THIS TIME..
NO, SIR! WHEN I GET STARTED ON SOMETHING REALLY WORTH WHILE I NEVER GIVE UP!

IF YOU'RE GOING TO COUNT ALL THESE STARS, I THINK I'D BETTER HELP YOU..

WELL! I APPRECIATE THIS, CHARLIE BROWN
HAVE YOU COUNTED THAT LITTLE ONE UP THERE?

WHICH LITTLE ONE? THAT ONE?
NO, THAT LITTLE ONE OVER THERE..
OVER THERE?
NO, THERE..

YOU MEAN THAT LITTLE ONE NEXT TO THAT CHARTREUSE ONE?
NO, THAT LITTLE ONE RIGHT THERE
YOU MEAN RIGHT THERE?

NO, RIGHT THERE..RIGHT UP THERE..
THERE? UP THERE?
NO, NO, THERE!
THERE? THERE?
NO! THERE!
THERE?
YES! THERE!

WHAT ABOUT IT?
SCHULZ

ALL YOU HAVE TO DO IS KEEP YOUR EYE ON THE BALL..

GIRLS ARE A NUISANCE SOMETIMES, BUT IT'S ALWAYS A GOOD IDEA TO HUMOR THEM..

O.K.. TRY AN' HIT IT..

POW!

KLUNK!

A HOME RUN
OOF!

WELL? DO YOU THINK I'M GOOD ENOUGH TO PLAY ON YOUR TEAM, CHARLIE BROWN?
YOU'LL NEVER PLAY ON MY TEAM!

BUT WHY NOT?
BECAUSE I'M GIVING UP THE GAME..
SCHULZ

BIG KIDS DRIVE ME CRAZY...

WELL, I'LL BE!

I CAN'T BELIEVE IT!

ALL THESE TOYS, AND NOBODY AROUND
NO BIG KIDS TO TAKE THINGS AWAY FROM ME JUST WHEN I'M STARTING TO HAVE FUN...

I CAN'T STAND BIG KIDS..
I CAN'T GET OVER IT.. ALL THESE TOYS AND NOBODY AROUND...

OH GOOD GRIEF! HERE THEY COME!

BIG KIDS!!

SIGH
SCHULZ

DID YOU KNOW THAT LUCY WAS GOING TO DANCING SCHOOL?
UH HUH... IT'S JUST ONE MORE WAY FOR HER MOTHER TO GET HER OUT OF THE HOUSE...

ASK HER TO DO A FEW STEPS FOR US..

HOW'S DANCING SCHOOL, LUCY?
FINE!

HOW ABOUT SHOWING US WHAT YOU'VE LEARNED?
WELL ...I'M NOT SURE I CAN REMEMBER EVERYTHING, BUT...

SCHULZ
THAT COST MY DAD TWELVE DOLLARS!

I APPRECIATE YOUR COMING OVER TO HELP ME, CHARLIE BROWN...

THE FIRST THING WE DO IS GET YOU A STOOL TO SIT ON..
?

THIS IS SOMETHING I LEARNED FROM VIRGIL THOMSON

YOU SIT RIGHT THERE, SEE, AND THEN I'LL PAINT YOUR MUSICAL PORTRAIT..
OH, I GET IT..YOU'LL TRY TO CAPTURE MY PERSONALITY IN MUSIC...RIGHT?

RIGHT...ARE YOU READY?
I'M READY...THIS IS VERY FLATTERING..

MINE IS THE TYPE OF PERSONALITY THAT WILL PROBABLY INSPIRE AN HEROIC SYMPHONY...

?

I DON'T HEAR A THING...

!

SIGH
SCHULZ

Z

GIMME THAT BLANKET!

WHEW

?

SCHULZ

?

THERE...NOW WE'RE ALL SET...

HERE, LINUS... TAKE A CARD.. ANY CARD...

NOW, I'M GOING TO SHOW YOU A LITTLE....A...A... I'M...I'M.....

HERE...TAKE A CARD...ANY CARD..
SCHULZ

MAN! THAT KITE IS REALLY UP THERE!!

LOOK, SCHROEDER...HAVE YOU EVER SEEN A KITE UP SO HIGH?

I'VE GOT TO HAND IT TO YOU, LUCY...I ALWAYS THOUGHT YOU WERE KIND OF DUMB, BUT ANYONE WHO CAN GET A KITE UP THAT HIGH IS ALL RIGHT IN MY BOOK! YES, SIR!

GOING TO HAUL IT IN NOW, EH? THAT'S PROBABLY A GOOD IDEA...A KITE SHOULDN'T BE KEPT UP IN THE AIR TOO LONG...ESPECIALLY ONE THAT WAS THAT HIGH...

?
?

SCHULZ

I THOUGHT I HEARD HOOFBEATS?

LOOK OUT! HERE HE COMES AGAIN!!

GOOD GRIEF!?
ZOOM!

!
!
ZOOM!

ZOOM!

NO, NO, SNOOPY! NOT THOSE!!

WHAM!

SCHULZ
BOY, WHAT A STUPID DOG!

SIGH!

AH HA HA HA!
HO HO HO!
!

BONK!
SCHULZ

HI, FUSSBUDGET... IS LINUS HOME?
HE'S IN THE OTHER ROOM..

IS THAT A BALL, OR ARE YOU CARRYING YOUR HEAD UNDER YOUR ARM?
WHY DON'T YOU GO THROW YOURSELF ON THE FLOOR, FUSSBUDGET?

EVER SEEN A BASKETBALL, BEFORE, LINUS?

BASKETBALL IS A GREAT GAME, I TELL YOU! A PERFECT COMBINATION OF SPEED AND SKILL, AND...

!

BUMPETY
BUMPETY
BUMPETY
bumpety
BUMPETY
BUMPETY
bumpety
bumpety
BUMPETY
BUMP
BUMP
Bumpety
BUMPETY
BUMPETY
bumpety
BUMPETY
BUMPETY
BUMP
BOMP

SWISH!
THUMP
PLUNK!

THERE'S NOTHING MORE ANNOYING THAN A SMART-ALECKY KID!
SCHULZ

HEY! COME BACK HERE!

HE'S GOT OUR BALL AGAIN!
SNOOPY!

YOU COME BACK HERE WITH THAT BALL!!

YOU CRAZY DOG!
LOOK WHERE HE WENT! NOW WE'LL NEVER GET HIM!

SNOOPY'S GOT OUR BALL, AND WON'T GIVE IT BACK TO US..
HE WON'T, EH? WHERE IS HE?
HE'S SITTING OVER THERE IN THE MIDDLE OF THE YARD

IN THE MIDDLE OF THE YARD?! THEN WHY DON'T YOU JUST GO TAKE IT? HE WON'T BITE...
WE CAN'T.. WE JUST CAN'T..
YOU DON'T UNDER-STAND...

I DON'T SEE WHY YOU CAN'T TAKE A BALL FROM A DOG WHO WON'T BITE AND IS JUST SITTING IN THE MIDDLE OF THE YARD...

OH...
SCHULZ

WHAP!

WHOP!

WHANG!

ALL RIGHT... I'VE GOT IT UP HERE AS FAR AS THE NET...NOW WHAT?
SCHULZ

WATCH ME HIT THAT TREE SNOOPY..

?
?

PLOP!

YOU GOT IN THE WAY!
SCHULZ

C'MON, SNOOPY...YOU CAN SIT RIGHT BEHIND ME..

ARE YOU READY?

HERE WE GO!!

HANG ON!

DOWN! DOWN! DOWN!

RACING LIKE THE WIND...

WE MADE IT!!
!

SHALL WE TRY IT AGAIN RIGHT AWAY, OR DO YOU WANT TO WAIT UNTIL YOU CATCH YOUR BREATH?
SCHULZ

POOF!

WHOP!

BASEBALL IS NO LONGER A HITTER'S GAME..
SCHULZ

Joker
Joker

WATCH ME, LINUS, AND I'LL SHOW YOU HOW TO BUILD A HOUSE OF CARDS...

IT'S KIND OF HARD AT FIRST, BUT AFTER YOU CATCH ON, IT... **RATS!**

C'MON! STAND UP THERE..RATS! C'MON, NOW...THAT'S THE WAY.. **RATS! RATS! RATS!**

STEADY...STEADDY.. STEAAAADDDDY...

There! HOW'S THAT !?

!
SCHULZ

I CAN'T STAND SMART-ALECKY KIDS!

SIX HUNDRED! AN ALL-TIME RECORD!

WHEEEEEEEE

NOBODY CAN JUMP ROPE BETTER THAN I!

NOBODY! NOBODY! NOBODY!

I'M THE BEST THERE IS! THE BEST, THE BEST, THE VERY BEST..

?
SIX HUNDRED AN NINETY EIGHT.. SIX HUNDRED AN' NINETY NINE.. **SEVEN HUNDRED**.. SEVEN HUNDRED AN' ONE.. SEVEN HUNDRED AN' TWO..

!
SEVEN HUNDRED AN' THREE.. SEVEN HUNDRED AN' FOUR..

MY OWN BABY BROTHER...
SCHULZ

COOKIE

CHOMP CHOMP
COOKIES

CHOMP CHOMP CHOMP
COOKIES

CHOMP CHOMP
COOKIES

CHOMP CHOMP CHOMP
COOKIES

CHOMP CHOMP CHOMP
COOKIES

CHOMP CHOMP

GRROWRRRRRRR
CHOMP CHOMP

SIGH
CHOMP CHOMP CHOMP
SCHULZ

HEY!

COME BACK HERE!

PATTY, HAVE YOU SEEN MY PLASTIC SWIMMING POOL? I WAS JUST GOING TO FILL IT WITH WATER WHEN THE WIND BLEW IT AWAY..

'FLYING SAUCERS ARE REAL,' IT SAYS HERE...'AUTHENTIC REPORTS INDICATE'..

AAK!

THEY GOT ME! THEY GOT ME!
?

HELP!
RIP!

A MARTIAN!

HE POINTED HIS FLAME-THROWER RIGHT AT ME!
ONE NEW SWIMMING POOL.. COMPLETELY SHOT!
SCHULZ

AHEM!

HE'S SO CUTE... SIGH

I'LL BET IF WE WERE TO GET MARRIED SOME DAY, SCHROEDER, WE'D BE VERY HAPPY...

WHILE YOU WERE PRACTICING THE PIANO, I'D BE IN THE KITCHEN MAKING YOUR BREAKFAST...

THEN I'D BRING IT IN LIKE THIS, AND SET IT ALL OUT NICE, AND PROP UP YOUR FAVORITE NEWS-PAPER, AND POUR YOUR COFFEE...

WOULDN'T THAT BE ROMANTIC?

NO!

MUSICIANS AREN'T REAL PEOPLE!
SCHULZ

GEE, IT'S COLD IN HERE...

SCHULZ

SOMETIMES I THINK I'D LIKE TO BE ALMOST ANYTHING BUT A DOG..

BIRDS ARE THE PEOPLE I ENVY THE MOST...

BOY! THERE'S THE LIFE!

SIGH!

?

SCHULZ

WHOSE NEW TRICYCLE?
THAT BELONGS TO LINUS...

DOES THIS BELONG TO LINUS, TOO?
SURE..

AND LOOK AT THIS NICE CAR...HE GOT THAT FOR HIS BIRTHDAY...
WOW!

COME ON IN THE HOUSE...I'LL SHOW YOU A FEW OTHER THINGS...

SEE? HE HAS GAMES, BOOKS, RECORDS....EVERYTHING!

SO YOU KNOW WHAT HE PLAYS WITH ALL DAY LONG?

THE VACUUM CLEANER!
SCHULZ

?

SCHULZ

NO!
OH, COME ON, CHARLIE BROWN..BE A GOOD SPORT..

BE A GOOD SPORT?!

WHY SHOULD I PLAY CHECKERS WITH SOMEONE WHO'S BEATEN ME EIGHT THOUSAND GAMES IN A ROW?

WELL, I'M TRYING TO MAKE IT AN EVEN TEN THOUSAND

COME ON, CHARLIE BROWN.. YOU HAVEN'T GOT ANYTHING ELSE TO DO...

OH, ALL RIGHT... GO AHEAD..... START ANOTHER GAME..
GOOD.. I ENJOY PLAYING SO MUCH..EVEN IF YOU DO GET MAD WHEN YOU LOSE..

BEAT AGAIN! HA HA HA WELL, THAT'S THE WAY IT GOES, I GUESS...EIGHT THOUSAND AND THREE GAMES IN A ROW..
SHALL I STAND BACK NOW WHILE YOU RANT AND RAVE?

WHY, NO...WHY SHOULD I RANT AND RAVE? IT'S ONLY A GAME.. HA! HA! I DON'T MIND..HA! HA! IT'S ONLY A GAME..HA! HA!

I QUIT!!!! I HATE PLAYING WITH A POOR LOSER...

BUT I CAN'T STAND PLAYING WITH A GOOD LOSER!
SCHULZ

THAT'S THE WAY TO PITCH, CHARLIE BROWN, OL' KID!

KEEP THROWIN' 'EM, BOY! YOU'RE DOING GREAT!!

GOOD PITCHING, OL' PAL! KEEP THROWIN' 'EM IN THERE!

HEY, WAIT A MINUTE! YOU DON'T HAVE TO WALK OUT HERE EVERY TIME.. JUST THROW ME THE BALL..

LISTEN...IF THE OTHER TEAM EVER SAW ME TRYING TO THROW TO YOU....

THEY'D KNOW I COULD NEVER THROW AS FAR AS SECOND BASE!
SCHULZ

WHAT'VE YOU GOT BEHIND YOUR BACK, CHARLIE BROWN?
NONE OF YOUR BUSINESS!

I'LL BET IT'S A VALENTINE..
!

THIS IS FOR YOU VIOLET.. HAPPY VALENTINE'S DAY!

THAT DOESN'T SOUND QUITE RIGHT..

THIS IS FOR YOU, VIOLET.. HAPPY VALENTINE'S DAY!
?

HERE, VIOLET, THIS IS FOR YOU... HAPPY VALENTINE'S DAY!

I KNOW I CAN DO IT IF I JUST DON'T GET NERVOUS...

THIS IS FOR YOU, VIOLET... HAPPY VALENTINE'S DAY!

THIS IS FOR YOU, VIOLET... HAPPY VALENTINE'S DAY!

OOPS! THERE SHE IS!! EASY, NOW...DON'T GET NERVOUS..YOU CAN DO IT

THIS IS FOR YOU, VIOLET... MERRY CHRISTMAS!

AAGHH!

Thump!
Thump!
Thump!
SCHULZ

ONE, TWO, THREE...
THERE'S NO DOUBT ABOUT IT...I'M FIFTY YEARS AHEAD OF MY TIME..

FOUR, FIVE, SIX...

WHAT IN THE WORLD ARE YOU STANDING HERE FOR?

DON'T YOU KNOW IT'S STARTING TO RAIN?
OF COURSE, I KNOW IT! THAT'S WHY I'M HERE!! I'M COUNTING RAINDROPS!

'COUNTING RAINDROPS'! GOOD GRIEF! FIRST IT WAS STARS...NOW IT'S RAINDROPS!

!

OH, MY!
SCHULZ

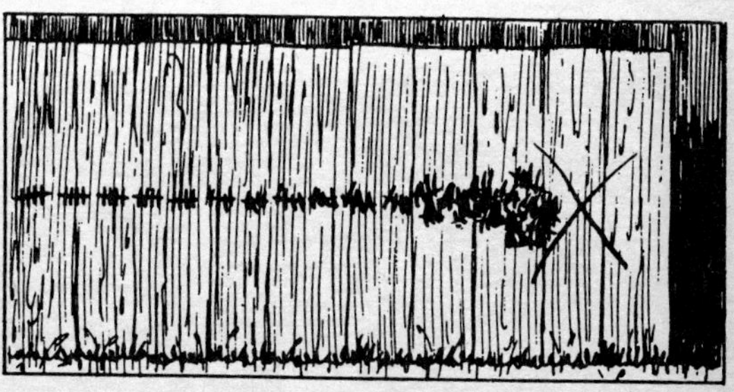

RATS!

LUCY, WILL YOU WIND MY TRAIN FOR ME?

THANK YOU!
WHIRR

WHIRRRRRR

RRRRRRR

SCHULZ
RRRRRRRRRR

OOPS!!
COMIX

HEH HEH HEH

EEK!

AAK!

HEH HEH HEH HEH

YIPE!

WHOOPS!

SOMETIMES IT'S KIND OF FUN HAVING A COLD NOSE!
SCHULZ

SCHULZ

THOSE GIRLS HAVE BEEN SITTING THERE ALL MORNING TALKING AND GIGGLING..

I'LL BET I KNOW WHAT'S GOING ON...

?
YOU GIRLS ARE TALKING ABOUT ME, AREN'T YOU?
IF YOU HAVE SOMETHING TO SAY ABOUT ME, WHY DON'T YOU SAY IT TO MY FACE?

WE WEREN'T TALKING ABOUT YOU, CHARLIE BROWN! NOW, GO AWAY!

HA HA HA HA!
HO HO HO HO HO HO!

NOW YOU'RE LAUGHING AT ME!!

OH, GOOD GRIEF! WE WEREN'T LAUGHING AT YOU! WE WEREN'T EVEN THINKING ABOUT YOU!!

HOW COME YOU GIRLS NEVER THINK ABOUT ME?

COME OVER HERE BY THE CURB...

I WANT TO TELL YOU A FEW THINGS YOU SHOULD KNOW..
?

DO YOU SEE THOSE HOUSES OVER THERE, LINUS? WELL, EACH ONE HAS A FAMILY LIVING IN IT JUST LIKE OURS

AND THERE ARE THOUSANDS OF HOUSES ALL OVER THE CITY... AND THERE ARE HUNDREDS OF CITIES ALL OVER THE STATE...

AND IF YOU STARTED TO WALK, YOU'D COME TO OTHER STATES WITH MORE CITIES WITH MORE PEOPLE, AND THEN YOU'D COME TO THE OCEAN!

AND IF YOU CROSSED THE OCEAN, YOU'D COME TO MORE COUNTRIES WITH MORE PEOPLE! MILLIONS OF PEOPLE!!

AND THEN THERE ARE ANIMALS, LINUS! THE FORESTS ARE FILLED WITH ANIMALS, AND THE OCEANS ARE FILLED WITH FISH AND THE SKY IS FILLED WITH BIRDS, AND..

AAUGHH!
SCHULZ

HOW CAN I TAKE YOUR PICTURE IF YOU'RE GOING TO SIT 'WAY OVER THERE? COME UP CLOSER..

NO, NOT THAT CLOSE! MOVE AWAY!

NOW DON'T, SCOWL, SNOOPY, PLEASE!
AND DON'T GIVE ME THAT SILLY GRIN!

AND DON'T TURN YOUR HEAD! LOOK AT THE CAMERA!

TRY TO HOLD STILL, SNOOPY...FOR ONCE IN YOUR LIFE SEE IF YOU CAN COOPERATE..

JUST ACT NATURAL.. SMILE PLEASANTLY..UH,HUH. THERE! THAT'S FINE... READY?

CLICK!

OH, I CAN'T STAND IT!
?
SCHULZ

KLOP

!

GIMME THAT BALL!!
HE'S GONNA SCORE!
GIMME IT, I SAY!!!

BY GOLLY, I'M NOT GONNA FOOL AROUND WITH YOU!
?
HOME! HOME! GET 'IM AT HOME!

I'M SAFE!
OH, GOOD GRIEF!

YOU DRIVE ME CRAZY!
SCHULZ

TAKE IT AWAY LINUS...HAVE A GOOD TIME!

WHAT A STRANGE LITTLE FELLOW HE IS....

DID YOU KNOW THAT YOUR BROTHER BORROWED MY CROQUET SET?

WHAT'S THE MATTER, CHARLIE BROWN? YOU WANT IT BACK ALREADY?

OH, NO..
I WAS JUST WONDERING IF HE HAD ANY TROUBLE GETTING IT SET UP...

I DON'T THINK HE KNOWS ANYTHING AT ALL ABOUT CROQUET....

!
BUT HE'S SURE GOOD ON THE HIGH HURDLES!
SCHULZ

?

SCHULZ

GEE, HE'S CUTE *SIGH* BUT HE DOESN'T EVEN KNOW I'M ALIVE..

AND SOMETHING'S GOT TO BE DONE ABOUT IT!

I'M GOING TO MAKE SCHROEDER NOTICE ME IF I HAVE TO KILL MYSELF TRYING..

HEY! HEY!
?

LOOKIT ME! I'M DANCIN'!

GET OFF MY PIANO!

GOOD GRIEF! SCRATCHES..SCUFF MARKS..FOOTPRINTS..
WHEW

SCHULZ
I THINK THAT POOR GIRL HAS LOST HER MIND..
I'LL PROBABLY NEVER GET MARRIED..

RATS..
SNAP!

RATS!
SNAP!

RATS!!
SNAP!

SIGH...

I JUST LEARNED SOMETHING...
OH?

NO MATTER HOW HARD YOU TRY, YOU CAN'T BEND A CRACKER!

THUMP THUMP THUMP THUMP

RIP!

CRASH!

SNAP!
TEAR!
BONK!
SMASH!

?
SCHULZ

AAUGH

SCHULZ

RATS

YOU MAKE ME NERVOUS SNOOPY..

WHAPETY WHAPETY WHAPETY
WHAPETY WHAP

!
GLUP!

HEY! LET GO OF THAT BALL

NO! I MEAN DON'T LET GO!

ZOOM!

YOU DRIVE ME CRAZY!
SCHULZ

!
CLUMP!

HEY!

YOU CRAZY DOG!!

GOTCHA!
WHAM!

LET GO!
LET GO, I SAY!!
LET GO!

WHEW WHAT A STRUGGLE..

I DON'T KNOW WHAT'S WRONG WITH THESE LIBRARY RECORDS... THEY ALWAYS SOUND SCRATCHY..
SCHULZ

DUM TE DA TE
DA TE DUM...

OH, OH!

I KNEW IT! EVERYTIME I BUILD A NICE SANDCASTLE PATTY COMES ALONG, AND KICKS IT TO PIECES...

WELL? WHY DOESN'T SHE GET IT OVER WITH?!!
?

THE SUSPENSE IS KILLING ME!

?

WELL, I'LL BE! SHE DIDN'T EVEN TOUCH IT! SHE DIDN'T..

!
POW!

SIGH
SCHULZ

YOU CAN'T BELIEVE EVERYTHING YOU HEAR, YOU KNOW..

WELL, YOU CAN BELIEVE **THIS**!

YOU **KNOW** I'M RIGHT, SCHROEDER..

IF YOU HAD ANY SENSE AT ALL, YOU'D ADMIT IT..

OH, YEAH?

YOU JUST SAY THAT BECAUSE YOU'RE STUPID, CHARLIE BROWN!

STUPID? LISTEN TO WHO'S TALKING!

YOU AND THAT **PIANO** OF YOURS ARE THE **STUPID** ONES!

PLINK PLINK PLINK!! ALL DAY LONG... **GOOD GRIEF!**

WELL, HOW ABOUT YOU AND THAT SILLY OL' COONSKIN CAP?!

AND HOW ABOUT THAT STUPID SHIRT WITH THAT STUPID STRIPE?!

WELL, AT LEAST, SCHROEDER, I DON'T HAVE YELLOW HAIR!

NO, BUT YOU SURE HAVE A ROUND HEAD!

WHAT IN THE WORLD IS GOING ON HERE?

WE'RE ARGUING OVER WHO WAS THE BETTER...BEETHOVEN OR DAVY CROCKETT!

WHO'S GOT A ROUND HEAD?
YOU HAVE!
?
SCHULZ

?

KLUNK!

SCHULZ

YOU STAND THERE, AND I'LL STAND RIGHT OVER HERE...
?

NOW YOU DO JUST WHAT I TELL YOU..

JUMP SNOOPY! JUMP!

NO! NO! NO! THROUGH THE HOOP! THROUGH THE HOOP!

COME ON NOW... JUMP THROUGH THE HOOP.. YOU CAN DO IT...

AH! I THINK HE'S GOT THE IDEA...HE'S GOING BACK TO GET A GOOD RUNNING START..

C'MON, SNOOPY! THAT'S THE BOY!! JUMP!!

SCHULZ

GIMME THAT MAGAZINE! THAT'S MY MAGAZINE!

!

BANG BANG BANG!

Mommy!
BANG BANG BANG BANG
BANG! BANG!

LINUS KEEPS SHOOTING ME! MAKE HIM QUIT IT!!
BANG! BANG! BANG!
BANG BANG

LINUS! YOU STOP THAT NOW!! BEHAVE YOURSELF!

AND PUT THAT GUN AWAY!

SIGH
SCHULZ

AN' TWO FINGERS WILL MEAN A 'DROP,' AN' THREE FINGERS WILL MEAN AN 'UPSHOOT,' AN'...

WE'LL NEVER REMEMBER ALL THOSE SIGNALS, BUT IT WON'T MAKE ANY DIFFERENCE BECAUSE HE CAN'T THROW ANY OF THOSE PITCHES..

!
WHOP!

!
POW

THAT MAKES THE SCORE NINETY-THREE TO NOTHING...

I'VE COME OUT TO HAVE ANOTHER CONFERENCE WITH YOU
WHAT DO YOU THINK WE OUGHT TO DO?

WELL, THE WAY I SEE IT, THERE'S NOT TOO MUCH TO WORRY ABOUT...

I'VE GOT A FEELING THAT THEY WON'T BE HITTING 'EM SO FAR ANY MORE...
WE'RE CATCHING ON TO THEIR WEAKNESSES, HUH?

NO, THE COVER IS ABOUT TO COME OFF THE BALL!
SCHULZ

PHOOEY!

YOU AND YOUR STUPID OL' BEETHOVEN!

SCHROEDER NEVER PAYS ANY ATTENTION TO ME...WELL, BY GOLLY, I'LL SHOW HIM! YES, SIR!

CHARGE!

SMASH

THERE!
WHAT DO YOU THINK OF THAT?

?

!

I'LL PROBABLY NEVER GET MARRIED...
SCHULZ

WHAM!

WELL? WHAT DO YOU THINK? SHALL WE DO SOMETHING ELSE FOR AWHILE?

WE MIGHT AS WELL...LET'S GO OVER TO MY HOUSE FOR SOME LEMONADE..

WHEW!

WHEN? WHEN? WHEN? WHEN? WHEN? WHEN? WHEN?

WHEN WILL I EVER LEARN?!
SCHULZ

HMM...

YOU KNOW WHAT? CHOMP-CHOMP-CHOMP
WHAT?

NO MATTER HOW HARD YOU TRY YOU CAN'T THROW A POTATO CHIP!
SCHULZ

?

WHAM

SCHULZ
YOU'RE THE ONLY PERSON I KNOW WHO CAN USE UP A WHOLE DAY IN FIVE MINUTES!